WHY DO LOBSTERS TURN RED

WHEN YOU COOK THEM?

Tasty Tidbits about
the Science of
Food and Cooking

WHY DO LOBSTERS TURN RED

WHEN YOU COOK THEM?

HERVÉ THIS

FALL RIVER PRESS

Compilation © 2009 by Fall River Press

This compilation contains selections from *Kitchen Mysteries:
Revealing the Science of Cooking* by Hervé This. Translation
© 2007 Columbia University Press; © Editions Belin, 1993
and *Molecular Gastronomy: Exploring the Science of Flavor*
by Hervé This. Translation © 2006 Columbia University Press;
© Editions Pour la Science 2002

This 2009 edition published by Fall River Press,
by arrangement with Columbia University Press.

Fall River Press
122 Fifth Avenue
New York, NY 10011

Book design by Modern Good, Matt Bouloutian & Vivian Ghazarian

ISBN: 978-1-4351-1977-2

Printed and bound in the United States of America

10 9 8 7 6 5 4 3 2 1

WHY DO LOBSTERS TURN RED

WHEN YOU COOK THEM?

EV

WO

WHY

ER
IDER

cookbooks advise against handling pastry dough too much? Once water is added to flour, the gluten proteins begin to absorb the water, forming a very tough, though elastic, network. Prolonged kneading makes the gluten proteins coagulate, producing a very tough dough.

TO PRESERVE THE AROMATIC QUALITIES OF FOOD,
TRY BRAISING OR COOKING IN PARCHMENT PAPER.
INSTEAD OF ESCAPING INTO THE AIR, THE

AROMAS
+FLAVORS

WILL BE TRAPPED AND SEEP BACK INTO THE FOOD,
CREATING A SUCCULENT SUCCESS.

Roasting is not intended to tenderize meats. It is a quick cooking process designed to

FLOOD THE MOUTH WITH FLAVOR

when one takes a bite. For the best roast, choose a tender cut from a young animal.

IDEALLY

most fruits and vegetables should be consumed as quickly as possible after harvest, but if that's not possible, store vegetables in the refrigerator. Corn and peas lose up to 40 percent of their sugars in six hours at room temperature. Once picked, asparagus and broccoli use their sugars to create indigestible woody fibers.

WHEN MAKING YOUR OWN JAM,
remember that certain kinds of fruits gel better
than others. Fruits with a large amount of
the gelling molecule pectin, such as grapes and
apples, yield better jam than other fruits
like strawberries, blackberries, and
apricots, which may need supplemental
pectin in order to set.

If you are serving a salad composed
of many different kinds of salad greens,

TOSS THE TOUGHEST VARIETIES FIRST,

and then add the tender varieties.

DO NOT ADD VINAIGRETTE TO SALAD UNTIL IT IS READY TO BE SERVED.

Oil penetrates the surface of vegetables and drives out the air, and with it, the vegetable's color.

It is not always necessary **TO** let wine **BREATHE**. Before deciding whether **OR NOT** to do so, taste the wine; if it tastes too severe, aerate it by decanting into a carafe. Otherwise, leave it in the bottle—unnecessary exposure to oxygen may cause it to deteriorate.

IF YOU'RE STORING WINE, KEEP IT OUT OF A SUNNY PLACE.

ULTRA VIO- LET RAYS

CAN STIMULATE CHEMICAL REACTIONS THAT WILL ALTER THE WINE.

IT IS WELL KNOWN THAT BEANS PRODUCE

GAS

due to the body's inability to break down
the sugar galactose.
To minimize this effect, let the beans
germinate or soak in water.
Doing so creates the enzyme galactosidase,
which destroys the galactose.

CONTRARY TO POPULAR BELIEF, HOT PEPPERS CANNOT BURN A HOLE IN THE STOMACH.

On the other hand, a sauce like Tabasco can produce an inflammatory effect, but this is due to the acetic acid in the vinegar, not the capsaicin in the pepper.

Hot peppers may set your mouth on fire, but they also stimulate salivation, activate digestion, and provide a feeling of well-being after a meal. In addition, they stimulate the release of endogenous opioid substances, which are similar to morphine in their effect on the pain-sensitive nervous system.

TO KEEP HOMEMADE PASTA FROM STICKING TOGETHER

AS IT COOKS, INCREASE THE PROPORTION OF EGG. IF THE PROTEIN NETWORK IS FORMED BEFORE THE STARCH SWELLS UP, THE PASTA REMAINS FIRM DURING COOKING AND DOES NOT STICK. AFTER STRAINING, COAT THE STRANDS WITH A LITTLE BUTTER OR OLIVE OIL TO KEEP THEM FROM STICKING TOGETHER ON THE PLATE.

DON'T
BOTHER
ADD
ING
OIL

TO PASTA COOKING WATER.
STUDIES SHOW THAT IT MAKES NO SUBSTANTIAL DIFFERENCE WITH
REGARDS TO AVOIDING STICKINESS. OIL IS USEFUL MAINLY AT THE
END, AFTER THE PASTA HAS BEEN DRAINED.

THE WORD

GAS TRON OMY

COMES FROM THE TITLE OF A GREEK WORK, *GASTRONOMIA*, WRITTEN BY ARCHESTRATUS, A CONTEMPORARY OF ARISTOTLE WHO COMPILED A SORT OF MICHELIN GUIDE FOR THE ANCIENT MEDITERRANEAN REGION.

EACH PERSON has a threshold for perceiving sweetness. What tastes like sugary coffee to you may be just sweet enough to someone else. In addition, some individuals are more sensitive to table sugar (sucrose), while others sense the sweetness in fruits (glucose) more acutely.

Do you want your tomatoes to
RIPEN MORE QUICKLY?

Tomatoes generate ethylene, which causes ripening. If placed in a closed container or bag, they will ripen more quickly.

Do you want your tomatoes to
LAST LONGER?
To prolong their life, put them a well-ventilated place, so that the ethylene can disperse.

Salty, sour, bitter, sweet…

UMA

...AMI?

Is there really a fifth taste? Substantial evidence exists to prove that there is a receptor for umami, the hard-to-describe savory, meaty flavor found in mushrooms, soy sauce, cheese, and meats, among other foods.

SALTED

FOODS HEAT UP MORE QUICKLY IN A MICROWAVE THAN UNSALTED FOODS. SALT CONTAINS IONS, AND THE WATER MOLECULES THAT HYDRATE THESE IONS, BY SURROUNDING THEM, HEAT MORE QUICKLY THAN ISOLATED WATER MOLECULES.

Hard, calcium-rich water will slow the cooking time of dried beans. To avoid this problem, simply add baking soda to the cooking water. It prevents calcium from binding the pectins, and it makes the water basic, which allows the pectins to separate. Boil the beans gradually to ensure that the exterior and center cook evenly.

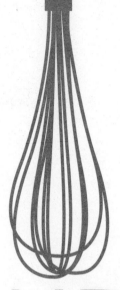

HERE'S A TRICK TO IMPRESS YOUR FRIENDS AND FAMILY: You can tell egg whites are whipped stiffly enough for a soufflé if they can support the weight of an egg in its shell without collapsing. If you're not in the mood for showmanship, just try turning the whisk

UPSIDE DOWN.

If the whipped egg sticks, it's ready to use.

A SOUFFLÉ WITH VERY STIFFLY BEATEN EGG WHITES WILL RISE HIGHER THAN ONE WHOSE WHITES HAVE BEEN WHIPPED FOR A SHORTER TIME BECAUSE STEAM BUBBLES HAVE A HARDER TIME PENETRATING THE STABLE FOAM OF THE VIGOROUSLY BEATEN EGG WHITES.

THE HUMAN PALETTE CAN DISTINGUISH AT LEAST 5 DIFFERENT TASTES IN ADDITION TO SEVERAL KINDS OF BITTERNESS.

BALSAMIC VINEGAR
FROM THE MODENA
REGION OF ITALY
IS THE ONLY VINEGAR
THAT HARMONIZES
WELL WITH THE

WINE

SERVED DURING
A MEAL.

Don't overcook cauliflower. Vegetables in the cole family—including mustard, Brussels sprouts, broccoli, turnips, and cauliflower—release

STINKY

sulfur compounds as they cook. The longer the vegetables cook, the greater the number of odiferous molecules released into the air.

EVER WONDER WHY SOME CHEESES SMELL AWFUL?

The microorganism used for the maturing process attacks the fats in the cheese and transforms them, releasing ammonia gas. It is this smell that repulses some, but it's essential to the evolution of creamy favorites such as Camembert.

COOKBOOKS RECOMMEND ADDING SALT ONLY
TO WATER THAT IS ALREADY BOILING BECAUSE SALTY
WATER SUPPOSEDLY TAKES LONGER TO BOIL THAN
PURE WATER. IT'S TRUE THAT ADDING SALT TO
WATER COOLS IT DOWN (BECAUSE THE WATER LOSES
ENERGY IN DISSOLVING THE SALT), BUT IT DOES NOT
AFFECT THE TIME NEEDED FOR THE WATER TO BOIL.
SO SALT AWAY WHENEVER YOU FEEL LIKE IT.

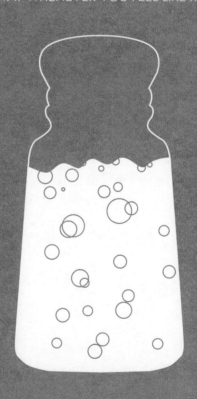

It is possible to center a yolk in a hard-boiled

egg, but it takes a bit of patience.

Put an egg in boiling water, and gently roll it

around the saucepan for ten minutes.

When you remove the shell, you'll

find that the yolk is perfectly centered.

TO AVOID A FONDUE

CHOOSE THE RIGHT CHEESE. WELL-RIPENED CHEESES LIKE CAMEMBERT WILL ALWAYS WORK WELL BECAUSE ENZYMES HAVE BROKEN DOWN THE CASEINS AND OTHER PROTEINS INTO SMALL FRAGMENTS THAT ARE READILY ABSORBED INTO THE WATER SOLUTION.

MARINATE YOUR MEAT IN RED WINE

INSTEAD OF WHITE. RED WINES DO A BETTER JOB OF PRESERVING THE TENDERNESS OF MEAT.

SALT

ALONE DOES NOT WILT SALAD GREENS.
AS LONG AS THE LETTUCE IS DRY, ADDING
SALT WILL HAVE NO EFFECT.

The best way to eliminate the unhealthy fat in meat is not through

BOILING, but by
GRILLING

and wiping the grilled meat with a paper towel or napkin. This method maintains flavor and removes excess fat, while boiling meat disperses its flavor (and nutrients) into the water while still retaining the fat.

The supreme cooking method is

BRAISING.

An initial browning stage kills microorganisms and creates a delicious brown crust. This stage is followed by a long, low simmering in a small amount of liquid that tenderizes the meat and creates a wonderfully aromatic and flavorful sauce. Instead of the meat flavors escaping into the liquid, the meat absorbs the best of the liquid and falls apart in the mouth.

THE TEMPERATURE OF YOUR TONGUE CAN AFFECT HOW YOU PERCEIVE FLAVOR.

For some people, heating the tip of the tongue can produce a sweet sensation, while cooling can cause a sour sensation or salty taste. Heating the back of the tongue produces a weak sweet sensation, but cooling this region can provoke bitter or sour tastes.

WHAT'S THE DIFFERENCE BETWEEN A SPICE AND AN **AROMATIC?**

The answer is not always straightforward.
A spice, such as black pepper, awakens the flavor
of the dish, but does not necessarily have
a strong odor. An aromatic, like saffron, serves
to enhance the smell of the food. But then
what's garlic? Both.

Use the freshest eggs possible for a successful

HOLLANDAISE

or béarnaise. The droplets of melted butter are better incorporated with fresh eggs than with eggs that are a bit older.

To avoid lumps in a béarnaise or hollandaise

SAUCE

add a small pinch of flour. The starch in the flour prevents the egg yolk from coagulating, and the sauce can even be boiled.

A PROPER ROUX TAKES A LONG TIME.

The starch molecules need time to break down into smaller sugars, increase their thickening power, and decrease their floury taste. To speed the process, try using potato starch, which gels at a lower temperature and has a less floury taste.

Why are fats essential in sauces? They coat the flour particles and keep them from lumping in the liquid, and they also give the sauce a

SMOOTH MOUTH FEEL.

Drink WATER, rather than wine, with salad. The acidity in the salad dressing destroys the taste of the WINE.

WHISKEY can be improved

by placing sticks of wood inside the bottle and allowing the liquor to age. It is crucial, however, that the wood is dry and not green, as wood contains aesculin, a substance that is bitter in green wood, but becomes sweet in dry wood.

PLAIN AND SIMPLE:
FAT IS WHAT GIVES FOOD ITS

FLAVOR.

TO TEST THIS THEORY,
TRY COOKING BEEF IN DUCK FAT.
THE RESULTING DISH WILL TASTE LIKE A
CROSS BETWEEN THE TWO MEATS.

TO SEASON THE WHITE OF A HARD-BOILED EGG,

add salt to the boiling water. It penetrates the shell, imparting flavor to an otherwise tasteless material.

DON'T FOR- GET THE SALT!

SALT BOOSTS BOTH THE ODOR AND FLAVOR OF FOOD BECAUSE IT MAKES IT EASIER FOR AROMATIC MOLECULES TO SEPARATE THEMSELVES FROM THE FOOD.

Another reason to CHEW slowly and enjoy your food: The more you CHEW, the more aromatic molecules are released from the food.

You'll perceive more flavors than someone who gobbles everything down.

WHY DO SHRIMP AND LOBSTER TURN RED WHEN COOKED?

These sea creatures contain a red-colored molecule called astaxanthin, the color of which does not appear in living animals. When seafood is cooked, it breaks up the bonds shielding the astaxanthin and the red color appears.

BLOWING ON

soup

WILL COOL IT FASTER THAN STIRRING IT.
THE PHENOMENON IS THE SAME AS THE
ONE YOU EXPERIENCE WHEN YOU
EMERGE FROM A DIP IN THE OCEAN ON
A WINDY DAY. BY EVAPORATING THE WATER
ON YOUR SKIN, THE WIND COOLS YOU.

TO PUT OUT THE FIRE IN YOUR
MOUTH FROM EATING A

TOO-HOT

PEPPER, DON'T DRINK WATER. INSTEAD, EAT SOME-
THING WITH FAT IN IT. CAPSAICIN IS FAT-SOLUBLE, SO
DRINKING WATER WON'T STOP THE BURN.

WHEN SEPARATING EGG WHITES FOR A RECIPE,
MAKE SURE NOT TO INCORPORATE ANY BIT OF

YOLK.

THE MOLECULES IN THE YOLK WILL
BOND TO THE MOLECULES IN THE

WHITES

AND IMPEDE THE WHITES' LEAVENING POWER.

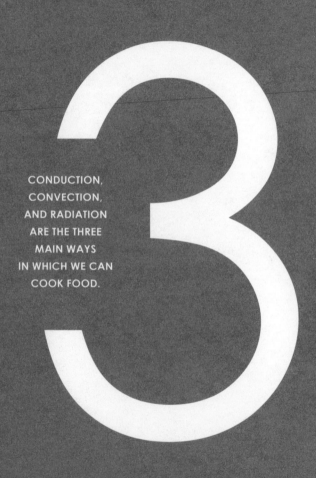

CONDUCTION,
CONVECTION,
AND RADIATION
ARE THE THREE
MAIN WAYS
IN WHICH WE CAN
COOK FOOD.

1. CONDUCTION

occurs when a solid is heated, such as when a metal spoon is left in boiling water.

2. CONVECTION

creates currents that circulate and distribute heat. If you place a pot of water on the stove, the water is heated first from the bottom. Because it is less dense than the cold water above it, hot water rises and is replaced by the cold water, which is in turn heated.

3. RADIATION

is the principle behind roasting. A fire or a grill emits invisible infrared heat rays that are absorbed by the meat. A microwave also cooks with radiation, but in this case, the waves actually penetrate the food much like sun through a glass window.

For a successful roast over a fire,

HEAT THE MEAT IN FRONT OF THE FLAME

rather than directly over it. If placed over the flame, smoke will overcome the flavor of the meat itself.

It's counterintuitive, but

HOT WATER FREEZES MORE QUICKLY THAN COLD WATER.

Three effects come in to play. **FIRST**, convection: the movement of the liquid at the top is not the same as at the bottom, forcing a flow that homogenizes the solution. **SECOND**, cold water dissolves more gas than hot water; with the gases removed, hot water cools more quickly. **THIRD**, a hot solution loses more water through evaporation, so in the end, there is less water to cool.

It's an old wives' tale
that mixing

OIL

and unclarified butter
raises the smoking point of oil.

It's best
to use clarified

BUTTER,

which can withstand a higher
temperature without burning.

ALWAYS USE DRY MEAT FOR FRYING.

IF THERE IS WATER ON THE MEAT, HEAT IS WASTED AS THE WATER MUST EVAPORATE BEFORE FRYING EVEN BEGINS.

To retain the most juices when grilling a steak, cook with high heat; don't salt or prick the meat until it's done; and eat it quickly after grilling.

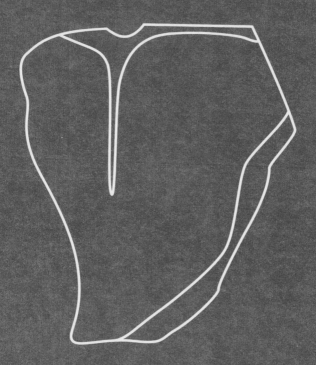

AVOID

COOKING MEAT IN THE MICROWAVE. THE WATER MOLECULES IN THE MEAT ARE HEATED AND VAPORIZED, RESULTING IN A BLAND, TOUGH MEAL. IN ADDITION, THE MEAT WILL TURN GRAYISH-BROWN BECAUSE THE TEMPERATURE STAYS BELOW 212°F, THE POINT AT WHICH OXYMYOGLOBIN WOULD BE DENATURED.

DID YOU EVER EAT BUTTER THAT TASTED LIKE THE REFRIG- ERATOR?

BUTTER ACQUIRES THAT UNPLEASANT TASTE BECAUSE MANY AROMATIC MOLECULES ARE SOLUBLE IN FATS.

WHY DOES WATER CAUSE HOT OIL TO SPATTER?
When water is suddenly immersed into oil at a temperature much higher than its vaporization point, it expands violently, spattering fat everywhere. The moral of the story: when frying, make sure the food is

DRY.

Don't be afraid of using

A LOT
OF
OIL

to fry foods. A large quantity of oil will maintain its temperature better when cold pieces of food are added to it. The hotter the oil, the more quickly a crust is formed, which prevents penetration of the oil into the food itself. If you fry foods in an insufficient quantity of oil that is too cool, the food will soak up oil like a sponge.

A sauce thickened with flour should not be heated at too high a temperature because it will partially reliquefy if it boils.

LOW&

is the way to go.

SLOW

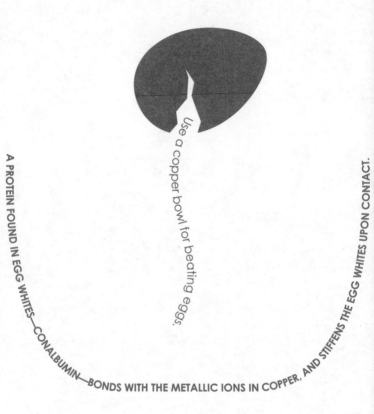

Use a copper bowl for beating eggs.

A PROTEIN FOUND IN EGG WHITES—CONALBUMIN—BONDS WITH THE METALLIC IONS IN COPPER, AND STIFFENS THE EGG WHITES UPON CONTACT.

ANY DISH THAT USES EGGS TO PUFF UP—

such as soufflés, macaroons, and quenelles—must be heated from below. Eggs contain water, and water evaporates during cooking. Steam becomes trapped and pushes the egg mixture up. If heated from above, the water would simply evaporate and escape.

To freeze vegetables successfully, you must first blanch them in boiling water to stop all enzymatic and chemical

HOT

activity. Follow this with a quick immersion in cold water to stop the cooking process.

COLD

WOODEN
SPOONS

DO NOT CONDUCT HEAT, SO THEY CAN BE HANDLED
WITHOUT BURNING THE FINGERS OF THE COOK.
THEY ARE ALSO SAFE TO USE ON NON-STICK PANS, AS
92THEY WILL NOT SCRATCH DELICATE PAN SURFACES.

TO

PRES ERVE FRUIT

IN THE FREEZER, ADD SUGAR, ALCOHOL,
OR AN ASCORBIC ACID SOLUTION.
AVOID BLANCHING, WHICH WOULD CAUSE THE
FRUIT TO LOSE ITS FLAVOR AND TEXTURE.

MAKE SURE YOU

CHILL YOUR CHAMPAGNE OR WHITE WINE FOR AT LEAST SIX HOURS BEFORE YOU

SERVE IT. IT TAKES AT LEAST THAT LONG TO BRING IT TO THE

RIGHT TEMPERATURE (AROUND 52–54°F).

ON THE OTHER HAND, YOU SHOULD
BRING UP A BOTTLE OF RED WINE FROM THE CELLAR
MORE THAN AN HOUR OR SO BEFORE DINNER
IS SERVED, SO THAT IT CAN COME UP TO AROUND 64°F.

When

MAKING bread, use flour that

is a few months old. Aging creates

more elastic dough, which makes for

BETTER

BREAD.

TO GET THE FROTH IN

A BUBBLING POT OF JAM

TO SUBSIDE, ADD A SMALL BIT OF MELTED BUTTER.
IT WILL DISPERSE THE FOAM.

TO ELIMINATE THE CLEAR FILM THAT SOMETIMES APPEARS
ON A CUP OF BLACK TEA,

ADD LEMON.

THE ACIDITY OF THE LEMON DISPERSES THE CALCIUM CARBONATE;
ADDING MILK WILL INCREASE THE AMOUNT OF FILM.

TO FIND A

GOOD

quality commercial pasta, look for one with yellow-amber color that is made from a hard, high-protein wheat, such as durum.

MOST COOKBOOKS
ADVISE THAT GNOCCHI ARE DONE WHEN
THEY FLOAT TO THE SURFACE
OF A POT OF BOILING WATER, BUT IS THIS
REALLY TRUE? WATER VAPOR FORMS
BUBBLES THAT CLING TO THE

GNoCCHi,

CAUSING THEM TO RISE. HOWEVER,
SHEER BUOYANCY ALONE IS NOT
A RELIABLE SIGN THAT THEY ARE FULLY
COOKED, THOUGH FOR THE AVERAGE
COOK NOT BENT ON PERFECTION,
IT CAN BE A GOOD MARKER.
IN MOST CASES, IT IS NECESSARY TO KEEP
COOKING SLIGHTLY BEYOND THE POINT
AT WHICH THEY FLOAT.

COOL
JA

slowly, at room temperature rather than in the refrigerator, to maximize its gel. Gel is made of triple helixes that tend to intertwine themselves; warmer temperatures allow the helixes to untangle, which ultimately produces a firmer gel.

RED WINE OWES ITS COLOR TO VEGETABLE PIGMENTS CALLED ANTHOCYANINS. OVER TIME, THESE PIGMENTS REACT WITH THE TANNINS IN THE WINE, MELLOWING THEM AND IMPROVING THE TASTE OF THE WINE. AS THE WINE CONTINUES TO AGE, THE REACTION MAKES THE RED OF THE ANTHOCYANINS DISAPPEAR AND THE DARK TANNINS BECOME VISIBLE.

THIS EXPLAINS WHY RED WINES DARKEN AS THEY AGE.

THE BEST TEMPERATURE FOR STORING CHOCOLATE IS AROUND

57°F,

APPROXIMATELY THE TEMPERATURE OF A WINE CELLAR.
THIS WILL PRESERVE THE AROMA AND APPEARANCE AND KEEP
IT FROM GETTING THAT UNDESIRABLE WHITE FILM. JUST ALLOW
IT TO COME UP TO ROOM TEMPERATURE BEFORE EATING.

BREAD

FL**OU**R

away from humidity. Once water molecules

come in contact with it, they begin to

break up the maltose that the yeast needs

to feed on in order to rise. Bread made

from such flour will not rise properly.

DON'T ADD TOO MUCH FLOUR TO THICKEN A SAUCE

OR IT WILL RENDER IT TASTELESS. THE REASON IS THAT THE FLAVOR OF FOODS DOES NOT DEPEND SOLELY ON THE ODOR AND TASTE, BUT ON THE INTERACTIONS BETWEEN THESE MOLECULES. MOLECULES WITH NO ODOR, SUCH AS STARCH, BIND WITH CERTAIN ODORANT MOLECULES TO PREVENT THEM FROM ACTING ON OUR SENSES.

BEWARE

of reheating cooked vegetables in butter. The

BUTTER

will make the sauce oily. If the vegetables are sautéed, the butter will cause them to turn brown and dry out. Better to use a small amount of water—or a microwave.

You can apply the concept of

AIOLI—that delicious Provencal emulsion of garlic and olive oil—to other vegetables. Try a puree of shallots, onion, or zucchini whisked together with olive oil.

PROTEINS GIVE CHAMPAGNE ITS

THE HIGHER THE PROTEIN CONCENTRATION, THE GREATER THE
QUANTITY OF FOAM PRODUCED.

USE
VINEGAR

to minimize the messiness of a poached egg. When added to boiling water, the vinegar coagulates the outside of the egg more quickly, thereby constraining the yolk inside.

IF YOU WANT TO AVOID A STICKY MESS,

don't add reserved cooking water to mashed potatoes. Milk is what's needed to limit the swelling of the starch and give a smoother consistency.

IT IS POSSIBLE TO SALVAGE

CURDLED MAYONNAISE,

AS THE CURDLING IS SIMPLY A SIGN OF AN INCORRECT CONFIGURATION OF MOLECULES. TO DO SO, WAIT UNTIL THE OIL AND WATER SEPARATE, TAKE AWAY THE OIL, AND ADD IT BACK IN MINISCULE AMOUNTS WHILE WHIPPING.

AFTER IT HAS BEEN FILTERED,

A SAUCE SHOULD BE SKIMMED.

TO DO THIS, TILT THE PAN SO AS TO ONLY HEAT ONE POINT ON THE BOTTOM. THIS ESTABLISHES A CURRENT THAT DRAWS THE SOLID PARTICLES TO THE SURFACE FOR EASY SKIMMING.

TRY POACHING FISH

IN, YES, A MICROWAVE.
THE MICROWAVE WILL
EFFICIENTLY HEAT THE POACHING
LIQUID AND COOK THE FISH.

CARAMEL CAN BE PREPARED

QUITE EASILY IN A MICROWAVE.
TAKE A SMALL BOWL, PLACE SUGAR
AND A BIT OF WATER IN IT,
AND HEAT IT—KEEPING A CLOSE EYE
ON IT. CARAMEL RAPIDLY RESULTS
WITHOUT ANY TROUBLE WHATSOEVER.

TO MAKE MAYONNAISE,

THE INGREDIENTS MUST BE BEATEN TOGETHER VIGOROUSLY, AS TO BREAK THE OIL DOWN INTO THE SMALLEST DROPLETS POSSIBLE TO EASE ITS COMBINATION WITH THE WATER. ALSO, ALL INGREDIENTS MUST BE AT ROOM TEMPERATURE OR WARMER FOR EMULSIFICATION TO OCCUR.

DO NOT UNDERESTIMATE THE STRENGTH OF AN EGG YOLK

WHEN MAKING MAYONNAISE. A WHOLE YOLK HAS ENOUGH SURFACE-ACTIVE MOLECULES TO MAKE SEVERAL QUARTS, MUCH MORE THAN NEEDED FOR YOUR AVERAGE MACARONI SALAD. FOR A SMALLER AMOUNT OF MAYO, USE ONLY A DROP OF YOLK.

HOW CAN YOU TELL A RAW EGG FROM A HARD-BOILED EGG
WITHOUT CRACKING IT OPEN? TRY SPINNING IT.

A RAW EGG SPINS SLOWLY

BECAUSE OF THE LIQUID MOVING INSIDE IT, WHILE A SOLID,
COOKED EGG SPINS MORE EASILY. IF YOU DO NOT HAVE TWO
EGGS TO COMPARE, SPIN THE MYSTERY EGG AND THEN STOP
IT JUST BY TOUCHING IT AND RELEASING IT. A COOKED EGG
WILL REMAIN STILL; A RAW EGG WILL CONTINUE TO SPIN.

SAUERKRAUT REQUIRES a particular level of ACIDITY. To prepare,

mix shredded cabbage, salt, and water together. At about 65°F, a bacterium will begin to grow and release lactic acid (the characteristic flavor in pickles and other foods preserved in vinegar). After about two and half weeks, it will have reached the appropriate level of acidity.

ASPARTAME, A SUGAR
SUBSTITUTE, SHOULD NOT BE USED
IN COOKING. ON ITS OWN, IT IS
SWEET LIKE SUGAR, BUT WHEN

CO OKED

THE TWO MOLECULES
IT IS MADE OF—ASPARTIC
ACID AND PHENYLALANINE—
SEPARATE, AND PRODUCE
TWO DIFFERENT
(UNPLEASANT) TASTES.

ADD TEA TO MILK RATHER THAN MILK TO
TEA. BY DOING SO, THE PROTEINS
IN MILK REMAIN INTACT AND ARE ABLE
TO MASK THE TEA'S BITTERNESS.

FOR A TENDER THANKSGIVING

TUR-KEY,

TAKE THE BIRD OUT OF THE OVEN WHEN IT
REACHES APPROXIMATELY

158–160°F.

IF COOKED TOO FAR BEYOND THIS POINT, THE WATER
THAT REMAINS BOUND TO THE PROTEIN IS RELEASED
AND THE MEAT BECOMES DRY AND TOUGH.

For a more flavorful jam, be careful how

MUCH PECTIN

you add. Studies show that the firmer the jam, the

LESS FLAVOR

it has.

FOR WHIPPED CREAM, USE AS THICK A CREAM AS POSSIBLE,

and refrigerate the ingredients before beating. This maximizes viscosity, the resistance to liquification.

DO NOT STORE BANANAS IN THE REFRIGERATOR. THE COLD DAMAGES THE BANANA'S ENZYMES, WHICH TURN ITS SKIN BROWN. BANANAS AND OTHER TROPICAL FRUITS AND VEGETABLES SURVIVE BEST AT ROOM TEMPERATURE.

COOKING MYTH DEBUNKED: searing does not lock in juices. They will escape regardless.

What searing does is create a

DELICIOUS CRUST OF NEW TASTY MOLECULES

to enhance flavor. To prevent the juices from escaping excessively, let the roast rest for a few minutes when it comes out of the oven. The juices at the center will work their way toward the drier periphery.

Salt masks
bitterness more
effectively
than sugar.
Sodium

IONS

selectively suppress
bitterness while
intensifying
agreeable flavors.

THE RECEPTOR ON YOUR
TONGUE THAT SENSES SPICY
FOOD IS BOTH A CHEMICAL
AND THERMAL SENSOR,
WHICH IS WHY EATING SPICY
DISHES MAKES THE MOUTH FEEL
AS THOUGH IT IS ON

RE!

WASH YOUR CHAMPAGNE GLASSES BY HAND
AND RINSE THEM COMPLETELY.

ANY SOAP RESIDUE,

PARTICULARLY FROM THOSE DETERGENTS USED IN
DISHWASHERS,

CAN CAUSE CHAMPAGNE BUBBLES TO BURST.

WINES IN MAGNUMS AGE MORE SLOWLY
THAN THOSE IN SMALLER, 750 MILLILITER BOTTLES.
A PROPORTIONATELY LARGER QUANTITY OF
OXYGEN ENTERS THROUGH THE CORK WHEN
THE BOTTLE IS SMALL.

THE LARGER THE BOTTLE, THE LESS THE EFFECT

OF OXIDATION ON THE WINE.

TO REJUVENATE TARNISHED SILVERWARE, PLACE THE ITEMS IN A PLASTIC CONTAINER WITH ALUMINUM FOIL COVERING THE BOTTOM. FILL WITH BOILING WATER AND ADD A TABLESPOON OF SALT. THE SALT TURNS THE ALUMINUM INTO A CONDUCTOR; THE ALUMINUM LOSES ELECTRONS, WHICH THEN ATTACH TO THE SILVER, AND TARNISH-CAUSING SULFUR IN TURN ATTACHES ITSELF TO THE ALUMINUM.

Don't believe the myth that sticking a
teaspoon in the neck of a

CHAMPAGNE

bottle will stop bubbles from escaping.
Only a cork can do that. But once you've
opened a bottle, why not finish it off?

The next time you have a particularly
tough cut of meat,

TRY TENDER-IZING IT WITH PINEAPPLE JUICE.

The especially powerful enzymes found in
pineapple (as well as in papaya and fig)
break down proteins in meat, resulting in
an absolutely tender roast.

USE A VERY DRY, ACIDIC WINE IN A FONDUE.

Such wines have high concentrations of tartaric, malic, and citric acids, which help stabilize the emulsion of cheese and wine.

A SORBET SHOULD BE SMOOTH,

which means preventing the formation of ice crystals. This can be achieved through agitation, but only once the liquid mixture has reached 32°F, starting to freeze. If done before this temperature, stirring is useless because ice crystals are unable to form.

Many cooks fret over frying the perfect egg.

TRY THIS:
Stop cooking it as soon as it turns opaque.
Otherwise, all of the water in the egg
will evaporate and the white will be rubbery.

Hard boiling eggs does not require a lot of cooking expertise, but it can easily be done badly. For

PERFECT EGGS,

immerse them in water that is already boiling, allow the water to return to a boil, cook ten minutes, and place the eggs immediately into cold water. You'll have delicious eggs and will also avoid that unwelcome sulfur smell that comes from overcooking.

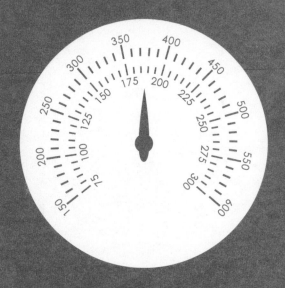

To help keep a soufflé from falling, keep the oven door closed. If the door is opened, the **SUDDEN DROP IN TEMPERATURE** will cause the air bubbles in the soufflé to contract and the vapor inside to condense—and your work of art to collapse.

FOR THE PERFECT ROAST,

follow these steps.

1. Sear the meat until it is nicely browned to enhance the flavor.

2. To retain the juices, keep the cooking time short by placing it in a preheated oven.

3. Season it only after completely cooking it, since salt will draw out moisture.

Q: Why does a steak

SIZZLE

A: It's the sound of liquid escaping from the meat and vaporizing.

When beating egg whites for a

MERINGUE,

add the sugar only after the stiff peaks have

formed. If the sugar is added too early,

the sugar dehydrates the proteins in the meringue,

and the whites whip up poorly.

IT'S A

MYTH

that adding a little vinegar or salt to egg whites will help them rise. Experiments show that the effect is limited, and it's best to stick to

WHIPPING.

DECIDING WHEN TO SALT A STEW CAN BE A TRICKY QUESTION. IF YOU WANT TO FLAVOR THE SAUCE, ADD SALT ONLY AT THE END. IF, HOWEVER, YOU ALSO WANT TO RETAIN THE FULL FLAVOR OF THE MEAT, ADD SALT AT THE BEGINNING.

REUSED OIL

HAS THE SAME POTENTIAL FOR DEEP-FRYING AS UNUSED OIL, BUT IT MUST BE FILTERED. IF UNFILTERED, REUSED OIL SMOKES IMMEDIATELY WHEN HEATED DUE TO THE FOOD PARTICLES THAT HAVE ACCUMULATED, AND THESE PARTICLES BLACKEN AFTER THEY HAVE SURPASSED ABOUT 160°F.

Don't peek at that lemon meringue pie by opening the oven door. The rush of cooler air will rapidly deflate the air bubbles in the meringue, and the meringue will solidify before the bubbles have time to reinflate. Instead, use an oven with a glass door and

BE PATIENT.

When preparing the **EGG WHITES** for a **SOUFFLÉ**, make sure that they are **FULLY SEPARATED FROM THE YOLKS**. If the two come in contact, the fat from the yolk bonds with the part of the egg white protein that normally coats the air bubbles, and prevents it from doing its job.

THE BEST SOURCE OF FIBER MAY BE...ALGAE.

The total concentration of dietary fiber in

wakame, for example, is as great as

75%

whereas Brussels sprouts—a very

high-fiber vegetable—are

60% fiber,

When making stock,

COVER THE POT.

As the stock boils, odorant molecules escape,
taking some of the flavor with them.
Even after cooking, when the fat is skimmed off,

THE FLAVOR WILL REMAIN.

USE A COPPER PAN FOR MAKING

JAM.

THE COPPER IONS REINFORCE THE
PECTIN GELS, WHICH FIRMS THE PRESERVES.

To avoid having a chopped avocado, mushroom, or apple turn brown before you are ready to eat it, add lemon juice or the juice of another acidic fruit. **CITRUS JUICE SERVES AS AN ANTIOXIDANT.** A knife damages a fruit's cells when it cuts through them, causing them to release their contents, particularly some enzymes that were enclosed in special compartments. The enzymes create melanins, resulting in a brown color.

CHEWING serves a

purpose greater than breaking food up into pieces

that can be swallowed. It increases the surface

area accessible to digestive enzymes, and it accel-

erates the assimilation of nutrients.

WHEN

MAKING STOCK,

KEEP IN MIND THAT MEAT LOSES ITS JUICES AT THE SAME RATE REGARDLESS OF WHETHER IT IS STARTED IN COLD OR BOILING WATER. THE TWO RESULTING BROTHS TASTE INDISTINGUISHABLE.

212°F

WHEN PREPARING A MEAT DISH IN A PRESSURE COOKER, IT IS OFTEN A GOOD IDEA TO BROWN THE MEAT FIRST. THEN, WHEN PLACED IN THE PRESSURE COOKER WITH LIQUID AND HERBS, THE CONCOCTION DOESN'T NEED TO RISE ABOVE 212°F, SINCE THE HERBS WOULD BE DEGRADED AT A HIGHER TEMPERATURE.

If you want to preserve the bubbles in your champagne, avoid wearing lipstick. Certain compounds in lipstick act as antifoaming agents. The effect is spectacular, as you can see by touching the foam in a glass of champagne with the tip of a lipstick.

UNLIKE STILL WINES, CHAMPAGNE SHOULD BE STORED STANDING UP,

RATHER THAN LYING DOWN. THE CORK'S MECHANICAL PROPERTIES ARE BETTER PRESERVED THIS WAY.

The main ingredient needed to make yogurt is...

GURT.

When a spoonful is placed in a pan of heated milk and cooked slowly for many hours, the bacteria in the milk releases the lactic acid in the yogurt, creating a single mass of yogurt.

THERE'S NO NEED FOR A DIFFERENT WINE GLASS FOR CHARDONNAY, CABERNET, AND ROSÉ. HABIT, NOT SCIENCE, PERPETUATES THE MYTH THAT RED WINE MUST BE SERVED IN GLASSES MORE VOLUMINOUS THAN THOSE USED FOR WHITE. RESEARCHERS HAVE FOUND THAT ONE SINGLE, WELL-CALIBRATED GLASS, KNOWN AS

THE ISO

(INTERNATIONAL STANDARDS ORGANIZATION)

GLASS, GIVES THE BEST RESULTS FOR BOTH WHITE AND RED WINES.

LOOK FOR A GLASS WHERE THE BOWL IS ABOUT TWICE AS HIGH AS IT IS WIDE.

The intensity and

COL-OR of WINE

depend on how long the juice is left in contact with the skins. The fullest, darkest, most tannic reds remain in contact with the skins for ten to thirty days. On the other hand, lighter reds are separated from the skins after just a few days. White wines are obtained by fermenting the juice alone.

For crispy sautéed potatoes,
cook the potatoes in water
for a few minutes so that they
acquire a gelled outer later.
This layer prevents starch granules
from absorbing too much oil
and allows the exterior to form a

PERFECT GOLDEN CRUST.

TO AVOID LUMPS IN EGG-BASED DISHES
SUCH AS FLANS AND QUICHES,
ADD A PINCH OF FLOUR OR STARCH.
FOR REASONS STILL UNKNOWN, THE
MOLECULES IN THE FLOUR BLOCK
THE CLUMPING OF THE EGGS' PROTEINS.

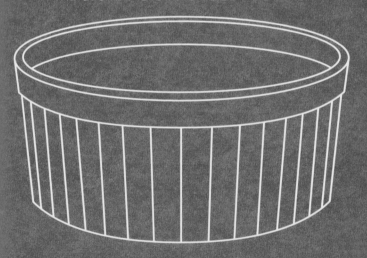

TO DETERMINE IF A BREAD DOUGH
HAS RISEN COMPLETELY,

POKE IT WITH YOUR FINGER.

IF THE HOLE PRODUCED DOES NOT IMMEDIATELY
CLOSE UP AGAIN, THE GLUTEN HAS BEEN
STRETCHED TO THE LIMIT OF ITS ELASTICITY, AND
THE DOUGH IS READY FOR THE NEXT STEP.

CO_2

DOUGH

BREAD DOUGH MUST BE KNEADED TWICE. THE SECOND KNEADING DISTRIBUTES YEAST SO THAT IT WILL MORE EVENLY RELEASE CARBON DIOXIDE DURING THE SECOND RISING PERIOD.

Did you know it's possible to cook without heat? Cooking with acids, for example, is simply a matter of placing the food—usually fish—in lemon juice or vinegar. The acid makes the proteins coagulate.

THE GREEN HIGHLIGHTS IN A YOUNG WHITE WINE

ARE DUE TO THE CHLOROPHYLLS EXTRACTED DURING FERMENTATION. OVER TIME, THIS COLOR WILL DIMINISH AS THE MOLECULE QUERCITIN OXIDIZES AND AGES.

IF YOU WANT A TENDER CUT OF MEAT,

BUY ONE THAT'S BEEN AGED.

SURPRISINGLY, THE TOUGHEST CUTS OF MEAT ARE THOSE THAT HAVE BEEN REFRIGERATED RIGHT AFTER SLAUGHTER.

WINE AGED IN OAK BARRELS

EXTRACTS TANNINS FROM THE WOOD AND REACTS WITH THEM, PRODUCING VARIOUS AROMATIC MOLECULES (LIKE VANILLIN).
↓

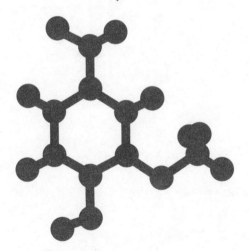

TO THICKEN A FLUID SAUCE, ADD

BEURRE MANIÉ,

AN EQUAL MIXTURE OF BUTTER AND FLOUR THAT

HAS BEEN WORKED TOGETHER BUT NOT COOKED.

TO AVOID A FLOURY TASTE, STICK WITH A CORN—

RATHER THAN WHEAT—FLOUR.

Make a roux-based sauce—like that used in gumbos and other dishes—thinner than

YOUR IDEAL SERVING THICKNESS.

By the time it reaches the table, it will have gelled to the proper consistency.

TAKE A QUICHE OUT OF THE OVEN WHEN IT BEGINS TO RISE.

The puffiness is a signal that water is evaporating and that the quiche is beginning to lose its smooth texture.

WHEN MAKING FRUIT PRESERVES, COOK THE
FRUIT IN A SUGAR SOLUTION EQUAL IN
CONCENTRATION TO THE FRUIT. THIS METHOD
WILL BEST PRESERVE THE FRUIT'S NATURAL
APPEARANCE. IF COOKED IN TOO LITTLE SUGAR, THE
FRUIT'S NATURAL SUGAR WILL PASS INTO THE
WATER, CAUSING THE FRUIT TO SWELL AND

EXPLODE.

IF COOKED IN TOO MUCH SUGAR,
THE SUGAR FROM THE CONCENTRATE RELEASES
THE WATER IN THE FRUIT, AND THE FRUIT

SHRIVELS.

AN EASY MARINATING TRICK:
PERIODICALLY INJECT
THE MEAT WITH A
KITCHEN SYRINGE FULL
OF MARINADE.
THE RESULTS ARE TERRIFIC
BECAUSE THE

MARI-NADE

WORKS FROM THE

INSIDE OUT

AND PREPARATION TIME
CAN BE SHORTENED.

JUST LIKE WINE,

CHEESE CAN HAVE TERROIR, THE SPECIAL CHARACTERISTICS A PRODUCT FROM A PARTICULAR GEOGRAPHICAL REGION CAN HAVE. COWS GRAZING IN DIFFERENT REGIONS EAT DIFFERENT PLANTS, EVEN WITHIN THE SAME PASTURE, RESULTING IN CHEESES WITH NOTABLY DISTINCT TASTES AND COLORS.

Do we perceive the taste of a dish less well after consuming a great deal of it?

STUDIES SHOW THAT OUR TASTE BUDS DO NOT EXPERIENCE FATIGUE,

so eat on!

TO TASTE WINE LIKE A PRO, TRY THIS METHOD: TAKE A SMALL SIP, AND PLACE THE WINE JUST BEHIND THE TEETH. IMMERSE THE TIP OF YOUR TONGUE TO DETERMINE IF THE WINE IS ASTRINGENT, SWEET, OR ACIDIC. THEN, TILT THE HEAD BACK SLIGHTLY AND PART YOUR LIPS TO BREATHE IN A THIN STREAM OF AIR TO AERATE THE WINE. EVEN MORE NEW FLAVORS SHOULD APPEAR.

CHAMPAGNE FOAMS BECAUSE THE YEAST IN THE WINE CONSUMES ITS SUGAR,

RELEASING CARBON DIOXIDE. THIS GAS IS DISSOLVED IN THE LIQUID, CAUSING IT TO BUBBLE WHEN THE CORK IS POPPED.

VINEGAR

WORKS WELL AS A MARINADE FOR MEAT BECAUSE
ITS FUNCTIONS ARE TWOFOLD: WHILE IT BREAKS
DOWN THE MEAT'S CONNECTIVE TISSUE, IT ALSO

PROTECTS

IT FROM PUTREFACTION.

TO THIN A SAUCE,

BEA

VIGOROUSLY, KEEPING A CLOSE EYE ON
ITS VISCOSITY. YOU CAN BREAK UP SWOLLEN
GRANULES OF STARCH UNTIL THE SAUCE
ACHIEVES A GOOD CONSISTENCY.

Warm pastry dough is more crumbly than the same dough when cool. Be sure to

WAIT

until a cake or tart is completely cooled before attempting to remove it from the pan.

If you store button mushrooms in the refrigerator,

DON'T CLOSE THE BAG. The circulating

air will preserve them, while excessive humidity will shorten their life.

WHY is WHEAT one of the only grains that makes a good bread dough? Because its protein composition is such that the gluten formed is resistant enough to make a leavened bread. It is both elastic, letting the bread expand, and viscous, meaning that it flows.

When preparing a dish that needs to cook for
a long period of time, don't add black pepper until

THE
END

of the cooking process. Pepper, when overheated,
gives off a strong, unpleasant taste.